Colin the
Goblin

Alan Cowsill & John Ross

To Mum and Dad
aka Joan and Alf Cowsill.
Thanks to Ste Norton,
Dave and Cherie.
A.C.

First published in Great Britain in 1998 by Mammoth
an imprint of Reed International Books Limited
Michelin House, 81 Fulham Road, London SW3 6RB

Text copyright © 1998 Alan Cowsill
Illustrations copyright © 1998 John Ross

Epix is a Trade Mark of Reed International Books Limited

The rights of Alan Cowsill and John Ross to be identified
as the author and illustrator of this work have
been asserted by them in accordance with the
Copyright, Designs and Patents Act 1988

ISBN 0 7497 3326 8

10 9 8 7 6 5 4 3 2 1

A CIP catalogue record for this book is
available from the British Library

Printed by Selwood Printing Ltd
Burgess Hill, West Sussex, Great Britain

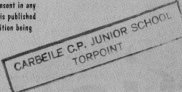

mammoth

Not all worlds are round. Some are flat, square, oblong . . . there's even one pear-shaped. Which is, oddly enough, what it's called.

Some people reckon Pear-shaped is a parallel world, others another dimension, some even think it's a distant planet. The only thing people can agree on is that it's really, really smelly.

Smelly ←

Not smelly →

It's ruled by ogres – big, bloodthirsty bullies, who dominate all the other races and even like to eat some of them. Especially goblins.

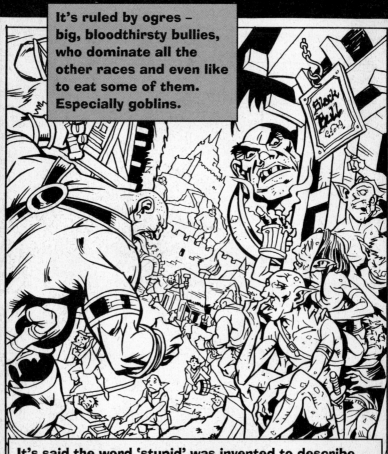

It's said the word 'stupid' was invented to describe goblins. As were 'spineless', 'cowardly', 'snivelling', 'gormless' and several far too disgusting to mention.

Not all goblins are stupid but most of them are. Some are so stupid they let the ogres use them as party snacks.
If that's not stupid I don't know what is.

A tubful of snot, five litres of rancid ogre vomit, two spoonfuls of earwax (human), a couple of pinches of that black stuff you find between your toes, a dozen live maggots, a touch of magic, something dead and rotting . . .

Meet Hopeless. Chief lackey, cook and bottle-washer of the ogre king.

. . . stir until it smells worse than the ogre king's ten-year-old knickers, and feed to a human, who will then turn into a tasty goblin. Now, where am I going to get one of them at this time of day?

Meet Sly. Thief, rascal and all round dodgy geezer. Once the greatest thief in Pear-shaped, now he's just another quick snack for the ogre king.

HMMFF, BMMFF GRRFFF!!

Ah, yes. Here's one I prepared earlier.

Force-feed the poor sucker the gunk . . .

Why can't ogres eat humans? Well, they give ogres terrible indigestion, whereas goblins go straight down and stay there.
This is a good thing for humans . . .

3

Good ol' Earth.
A few years
later. Enjoy it
while you can.

. . . And, finally, a new craze is
sweeping across the land as the
Ogre King chain of restaurants
opens for business.

People are going
burger-bonkers for the tasty free
food that their creator . . .

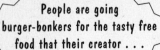

. . . Mister O.G. Reking
claims are made from things
that are too disgusting to
say over the air.

MY BURGERS WILL
MAKE YOU FAT, THEY WILL
MAKE YOU UGLY — BUT
THEY'RE SO TASTY YOU
WON'T CARE!

What a kidder.
Well, I don't know what's in
them, but they sure are yummy.
More news tomorrow.

Life-tip: Be warned —
there's no such thing
as a free meal.

Imagine the weirdest thing you can think of and then make it one hundred times weirder.

No, make it ten thousand times weirder and you still won't have anything nearly as weird as what happened to me.

I guess it all started with Elvis. No, sorry. Elvis was later. I should tell you about the burger bar incident, as it probably helped me save the world.

I found out later that someone had tripped me up on purpose to stop me eating a goblin-burger. But tripping up led to problems of its own.

Hey, watch where you're going you big . . . galoots . . . oops.

Meet Scud and Exocet. AKA Stevie Norton and Tommy Quarterman. Toughest kids in the history of Campion High School.

Wonder how much this'll hurt?

Hi, Scud, Exocet. Listen, I don't know if anyone's mentioned this, but you've both got fast-food growing out of your head.

The name's Colin Almond, by the way. I know, it's nuts. Very funny. Heard it all before. You'll be calling me ginger nut next.

Ouch, ouch ouch, ouch, ouch, ouch.

You ever have spells where everything goes wrong? Say you trip up, lose your homework . . . or decide that the day can't get any worse, only to find that it can?

Well that's not accidental. It's down to them. The goblins. Some can just pop in from their own world whenever they want to. They're everywhere, messing up our lives. It's what they do.

Hello, Colin . . . cut yourself trying to shave?

Like making you bump into your sister and her friend Katharine, when you've just had a really bad day and your nose won't stop bleeding . . .

I was just, er . . . there were these . . . lots of them too . . .

8

I found out their names later.

Sly used to be human and escaped from the ogre king's dungeon to join Happy and the rest of them. At least, that's what he claimed. Happy told me he's got a heart of gold. No one's sure where he got the heart of gold from, but he's definitely got one.

Happy's their boss and quite cool – but don't tell him I said that. Rumour has it that he once smiled, but that was a long time ago when he nicked this sword called Excalibur and stuck it in a stone to annoy Merlin the Magician. Tip of the day: never call him short.

The goblins had been on my back since we'd moved into the new house. They'd taken a liking to me.

You probably think that's not such a bad thing, but you're wrong . . .

You see, when one goblin takes a liking to you, lots of little things start to go wrong. Your favourite videos get screwed up. You lose your homework . . . embarrass yourself in public . . . accidentally trip the headmaster up and make him land in a pile of manure that's just been delivered to the school for the gardening club.

But when **seven goblins** decide to like you, well you have **real problems** . . .

What's that? You don't believe in goblins? Well, let me tell you something – they've been around as long as we have. If not longer.

Who do you think caused the Big Bang that wiped out the dinosaurs?

The first official sighting was at the Battle of Hastings when one was spotted helping King Harold.

Oops.

Cor blimey, mate — look at that thing coming towards your eye!

Ouch! They don't only mess with us in big ways though. Guess who made Southgate miss the vital penalty against Germany in the 1996 European championships?

That's right, goblins. They don't mean any harm by it. It's just what they do when they want a laugh. Who knows, maybe one's messing around with your life even as you read this.

Anyway, there's only one known way to avoid goblins, and it's been tried and tested for **years**.

15

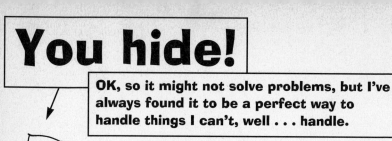

You hide!

OK, so it might not solve problems, but I've always found it to be a perfect way to handle things I can't, well . . . handle.

Mum decided I was ill after Becca told her how I lost it a bit and started talking about goblins and stuff. Mum must've been worried because she let me have two days off school. I spent most of the time hiding. You see, they wouldn't leave me alone!

Please, Colin. We, like, really need your help . . . and it's, like, important and everything. The whole world's counting on you. If you don't help there'll be plagues and disasters and loads of really gross stuff.

OK, maybe not plagues but there'd be lots of disasters . . . I mean, have you ever seen a goblin trying to fly a plane or run a power plant? It always ends with a bang. Usually a big one. And if the ogre king turns everyone into goblins . . .

Go away, you don't exist!

Happy explained to me what was going on. The ogre king wanted to turn all the humans on Earth into goblins. He was going to do this through his burgers, which contained a vile concoction of chemicals and magic that could turn the healthiest of humans into a useless, flabby sack of flesh . . .

. . . otherwise known as a goblin.

On Pear-shaped, most goblins do whatever they're told – even if it means ending up as food for the ogres. Only a handful stand up to them. If the ogre king's plan succeeded, most people in the world would become goblins and he'd be able to take control. *Then* he'd probably start snacking . . . possibly at a barbecue of some kind.

While Po tried to bring Becca to her senses, Happy explained the plan. Ogres can smell goblins a mile off. Most people can. But they can't smell humans. Which is why Happy wanted me to risk life and limb to get into the ogre king's castle, steal the antidote and blow up the gateway he was using to get to Earth.

Didn't I mention the antidote? According to Sly it could turn everyone back to normal. They thought I'd want to help them.

They were wrong.

Course I'm not going to help you. It's dangerous!

Do you want a squashed rat sandwich — it's got a fungus and phlegm sauce?

It was only then the true horror of it all hit me. I realised I had no choice. After all, I didn't want to live in a world of goblins. It would stink and the food would totally suck.

Oh yeah, and it'd probably mean the enslavement of the whole human race and stuff.

OK, I'll help . . .

Marilyn, do your thing.

Sure, honeybuns.

Mum, if anyone calls, I'll be on Pear-shaped saving the human race. Don't bother to wait up.

OK, dear. Have a nice time.

You're probably confused by now. I mean, goblins walking the Earth, an ogre king turning everyone into snacks. How could it all happen? Goblins are hard enough to believe in – but supercool, trans-dimensional, teleporting goblins with attitude?

Well, it's like this. Goblins are born with special gifts. For most the gift is that they're amazingly stupid – but a few, like Happy and co., can do really cool things. Marilyn, for instance, can teleport people from one world to another.

She's just not very good at it.

Silly me, I'm always getting the ground mixed up with the sky.

Can I just say something . . .

Luckily, a rubbish dump broke our fall. According to the goblins, that was a good thing. I begged to differ.

It stinks!

Yeah, cool ain't it?

What luck – I've not had any decent refuse for months!

Aaaaarrrrgh!!

DUNG

Look – fungus maggots. They're the best.

Crunch.

24

Are you a Goblin?

1. What's the first thing you do in the morning?

a. Try to get some more sleep?
b. Eat the fluff that's collected in your belly-button during the night?
c. Leap out of bed feeling totally refreshed, do 200 press-ups before running to school?

2. Which of the following would you rather eat?

a) Fish and chips?
b) Fresh elephant poo with a mashed worm sauce?
c) A lightly fluffed salad?

3. How badly do you smell?

a) I don't smell since I started using my dad's deodorant.
b) Like bad eggs mixed with gorgonzola cheese – only worse!
c) Like the air that I breathe after running up the mountain near my glorious home.

4) Which of the following most applies to you?

a) I'm human, me.
b) I'm a goblin, give me some snot.
c) I'm not sure what I am apart from exceptionally boring.

5. What's your favourite TV show?

a) Match of the Day?
b) Snot & Away?
c) Country File?

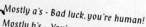

Mostly a's - Bad luck, you're human!

Mostly b's - You're a goblin – or a really smelly weirdo!

Mostly c's - You're so dull, I'm surprised you're reading this book!

And when I came to, everything had changed.

Did you know that goblins have little spider-like creatures living on their tongues and when they kiss, these creatures leap into the mouth of whoever they snog?

Well now you do. I always figured my first proper kiss would be with the woman of my dreams . . . or at the very least someone human.

Er, Marilyn, I think you can stop giving Colin the kiss of life now . . . He's, er, coming to.

What was even worse was that I enjoyed the feel of the little spider-like creatures dancing on my big, long, cold, pointed tongue. It could only mean one thing . . .

I'm a Goblin!

It's not so bad . . . I mean there's never been a ginger goblin before. Apart from Gary, and we don't like to talk about him.

Life-tip: Never, ever snog a goblin. Unless you really have to. And even then think twice!

35

41

When I came to, it was all over. The ogre king had taken the worst of the blast. There was no sign of him. Happy reckoned that he'd been blown to some distant corner of the galaxy.

And the headlines once again. The Ogre King chain of restaurants has collapsed after it was revealed that the burgers really did contain old socks . . . and a few other things I really don't want to think about.

Rumours of people turning into goblins and eating the garbage have been dismissed despite yesterday's strange scenes from Parliament.

It's good to be home.

The Prime Minister refused to . . .

I've had enough of you, ginger nut!

Hey, watch where you're going, you great big galoots!

Yeah, outside. Now. I'll teach you to call us galoots . . . and what is a galoot anyway?

You two are — and if you don't believe me . . .